G000153561

Invitation
Invitation
UN-BIRTHDAY SONG
Alice Chua

Playing Piano Is Fun

Alice Chua

Book 2

Student: ______________________________

Teacher: ______________________________

Published by
RHYTHM MP SDN. BHD.
1947, Lorong IKS Bukit Minyak 2,
Taman IKS Bukit Minyak, 14100 Simpang Ampat,
Penang, Malaysia.
Tel: +60 4 5050246 (Direct Line), +60 4 5073690 (Hunting Line)
Fax: +60 4 5050691
E-mail: rhythmmp@mphsb.com
Website: www.rhythmmp.com

ISBN 10: 967-985-617-8
ISBN 13: 978 967985617 0
Order No.: MPP-4003-02

Foreword

Playing Piano is Fun is a keyboard tutor series for beginners. It is designed to meet the developmental needs of children as they journey through the wonderful world of music. The tunes are specially composed by Alice Chua, and are based on the characters and subjects from the classic stories of *Alice's Adventures in Wonderland* and *Through the Looking-Glass* by Lewis Carroll. The literary experience is translated into the language of music with the intention of awakening the musical interests of children.

Playing Piano is Fun is a novel approach developed through the author's practical experience derived from teacher-pupil interaction. The large music font size captures the students' attention and helps them to focus. Meanwhile, pages are left intentionally without pictures to encourage students to further express their creativity by providing illustrations for the songs themselves. New elements are introduced incrementally and are incorporated progressively. Teacher's accompaniment is encouraged to enhance the musical experience, thus inspiring and motivating students. Some suggestions for the enhancement of the teaching elements can be found inside the front cover. In addition to playing piano, this series' unique approach includes listening, singing, transposing, harmonising, improvising and composing at an early stage.

A note from the author:

I wish pupils and teachers many fun and enjoyable music-making sessions with this series.

Yours musically,

Alice Chua, MA, FLCM, LLCM, Adv Dip Kodaly, Yamaha Teaching Cert. Grade 3.

About the Author

Alice is a passionate and enthusiastic musician, a versatile arranger, composer and music author. To this date, she has written many music books, used extensively in Asia and the United Kingdom. She is also an examiner with the London College of Music.

Whilst living in Malaysia and Singapore, Alice was Chief Music Instructor for Yamaha Music Asia. She opened new music schools in Singapore, Malaysia and Myanmar, and started music programs for pre-schoolers in Indonesia. This involved training teachers and designing music curricula suited specifically for each country. She frequently represented Malaysia in various international conferences hosted by Yamaha Music Foundation.

Now residing in London with her daughter, Alice divides her time between sharing her love of music with her students and invigilating examinations and competitions in Europe and the Far East. She believes that music should be played from memory, so that every child has the confidence to perform in any environment at any time, without needing to rely on a score. When children can express themselves freely in this way, it develops their ability to immediately engage their audience, and to derive from the music a personal sense of enjoyment.

Dedication

I would like to dedicate this series to my daughter Mitra and all my students, especially those who have chosen music as their profession.

I look back with fondness on our shared past, revel in our current projects and eagerly anticipate the future.

Contents

Date:________________

Part One — Space Notes in the Bass Clef

A-C-E-G: ***All Cows Eat Grass***. This sentence helps you to remember the four ***space notes*** in the ***bass clef.*** Let's locate these four notes on the piano.
In this lesson we shall play C note (2nd space) and G note (4th space). Can you play the G note with your thumb? Now place each finger on a white key (2-F, 3-E, 4-D & 5-C).
Are you ready to play *Stepping Up and Down the Looking-Glass?*

♪ Play & Sing Along

Let's play and sing the letter names of the ***treble clef*** notes and then the ***bass clef*** notes – sing an ***octave*** higher if the range is too low.

♪ Game:

Name these ***crotchets***:

♪ Pointers:

Are your hands in C position?
Do you have good hand shape?

Stepping Up and Down The Looking-Glass

Can you step up and down the Looking-Glass with Alice?

Date:________________

♪ Space Notes on the Bass Clef : A, C, E & G

Revision A-C-E-G: ***All Cows Eat Grass***. Let's locate these four notes on the piano.

Let's play the ***bass clef*** notes of *Skipping Up and Down the Looking-Glass*. Is your left hand in the correct position? (Hint: it is the same position as *Stepping Up and Down the Looking-Glass* on page 7).

♪ Play & Sing Along

Let's play and sing the letter names of the ***treble clef*** notes and then the ***bass clef*** notes – sing an ***octave*** higher if the range is too low.

♪ Games:

1) Write the four ***space notes*** in ***semibreves*** on page 62.
2) On page 9:
    a. Circle the C ***crotchets*** in the ***bass clef***.
    b. Draw triangles around the C ***minims*** in the ***bass clef***.

♪ Pointers:

Are both your hands in C position before you start playing?
Are you sitting comfortably?

Skipping Up and Down The Looking-Glass

Can you skip up and down the Looking-Glass with Alice?

Date:__________________

♪ Space Notes in the Bass Clef: A, C, E & G

Let's play the ***bass clef*** notes of *The Little Voice of Gnat*. Is your left hand in the correct position? (Hint: it is the same position as *Skipping Up and Down the Looking-Glass* on page 9).

♪ Play & Sing Along

Let's play and sing the letter names of the ***treble clef*** notes and then the ***bass clef*** notes – sing an ***octave*** higher if the range is too low.

♪ Games:

1) Write these four ***space notes*** in ***minims*** on page 62.
2) On page 11:
   a. Circle the stepwise notes ***E-D-C***.
   b. Circle the C ***minim*** in the ***bass clef***.
   c. Draw triangles over the C ***semibreves***.

♪ Pointers:

Are both your hands in C position before you start playing?
Are you playing ***legato***?
Are you keeping a steady speed?

The Little Voice of Gnat

Gently

Alice Chua

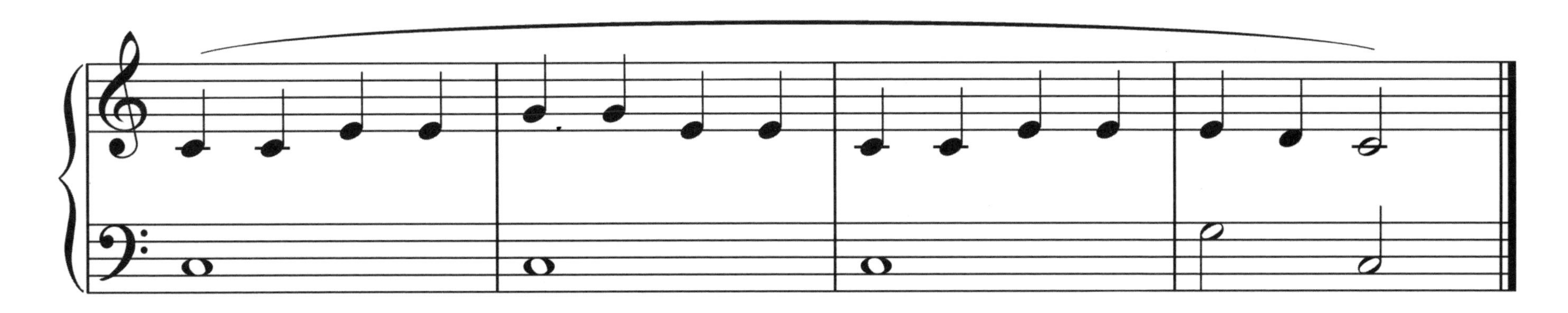

Can you draw a Gnat?

Date:________________

♪ Space Notes in the Bass Clef: A, C, E & G

Let's play the ***bass clef*** notes of *Rocking-Horse-Fly*. Is your left hand in the correct position? (Hint: it is the same position as *The Little Voice of Gnat* on page 11).

♪ Play & Sing Along

Let's play and sing the letter names of the ***treble clef*** notes and then the ***bass clef*** notes – sing an ***octave*** higher if the range is too low.

♪ Games:

1) Write these four ***space notes*** in ***crotchets*** on page 62.
2) Circle the G ***crotchets*** in the ***bass clef*** on page 13.
3) A ***semibreve*** equals:
   a. 2 / 4 / 6 / 8 ***minims***.
   b. 2 / 4 / 6 / 8 ***crotchets***.
   c. 2 / 4 / 6 / 8 ***quavers***.

♪ Pointers:

Are both your hands in C position before you start playing?
Did you rest at the end of ***bar*** 8?
Are you playing ***legato***?

Rocking-Horse-Fly

Can you draw a Rocking-Horse-Fly?

Date:________________

♪ Space Notes in the Bass Clef: A, C, E & G

Let's play the ***bass clef*** notes of *Snap-Dragon-Fly*. Is your left hand in the correct position? (Hint: it is the same position as *Rocking-Horse-Fly* on page 13).

♪ Play & Sing Along

When you can play this piece very well, let's add a C note below each G note in ***bar*** 4 and a G note above each C note in ***bar*** 8 in the ***bass clef***. Can you hear the beautiful harmony?

Let's play and sing the letter names of the ***treble clef*** notes and then the ***bass clef*** notes – sing an ***octave*** higher if the range is too low.

♪ Games:

On page 15:

a. Write the new notes in the ***bass clef***.
b. Circle the four stepwise melodic notes ***F-E-D-C***.

♪ Pointers:

Are both your hands in C position before you start playing?

Are you playing the notes in ***bars*** 4 & 8 simultaneously?

Snap-Dragon-Fly

Can you draw a Snap-Dragon-Fly?

Date:________________

𝅘𝅥𝅮 Space Notes in the Bass Clef: A, C, E & G

Let's play the ***bass clef*** notes of *Bread-and-Butter-Fly*. Is your left hand in the correct position? (Hint: it is the same position as *Snap-Dragon-Fly* on page 15).

𝅘𝅥𝅮 Play & Sing Along

When you can play this piece very well, let's add a G note above each C note in ***bars*** 2, 6, and 8 and a B below each G in ***bar*** 4 in the ***bass clef***. Your teacher will show you how. Can you hear the harmony?

Let's play and sing the letter names of the ***treble clef*** notes and then the ***bass clef*** notes – sing an ***octave*** higher if the range is too low.

𝅘𝅥𝅮 Games:

1) Write these notes on page 17 in the appropriate places.
2) How many ***crotchets*** make up the following?
   a. A ***minim***.
   b. A ***dotted minim***.

𝅘𝅥𝅮 Pointer:

Are you playing the double notes in the ***bass clef*** together?

Bread-and-Butter-Fly

Can you draw a Bread-and-Butter-Fly?

Part Two Higher C, D, E, F & G in the Treble Clef

The note written between the 3rd and 4th lines in the ***treble clef stave*** is a high C note. Your teacher will show you the position of these five notes in the ***treble clef stave***. Can you prepare your higher C position for the right hand? (Hint: Place Finger 1 on the higher C note).

♪ Play & Sing Along

Let's play and sing the letter names of the ***treble clef*** notes – sing an ***octave*** lower if the range is too high.

♪ Games:

On page 19:

a. Circle the stepwise notes ***C-D-E-F-G***.
a. Draw triangles over the ***minims***.

♪ Pointers:

Are both your hands in C position before you start playing?
Are you observing the ***crotchet rests***?
Can you remember the experience of playing the double notes with your left hand on pages 15 and 17?

Tweedledum and Tweedledee

Can you draw the twins?

Date:________________

♪ Notes in the Treble Clef: C, D, E, F & G

Revision Can you remember where the higher C note is in the ***treble clef stave***?

Can you prepare your higher C position for the right hand?

♪ Play & Sing Along

Let's play and sing with the letter names of the ***treble clef*** notes – sing an ***octave*** lower if the range is too high.

♪ Games:

1) Let's write these five notes in ***semibreves*** on page 62.
2) On page 21:
    a. Circle the stepwise notes ***C-D-E-F-G***.
    b. How many phrases can you find?

♪ Pointers:

Are you sitting comfortably?

Are both your hands in C position before you start playing?

Can you hear your left hand clearly?

Are you playing the double notes in the ***bass clef*** evenly?

Do you have good hand shape?

Tweedledum's - 'Nohow!'

What is embroidered on Tweedledum's collar?

♪ Notes in the Treble Clef: C, D, E, F & G

Revision Can you prepare your higher C position for the right hand?

♪ Staccato

Dots above or below the notes are called ***staccato markings***. You need to play these notes short and detached.

♪ Play & Sing Along

Let's play and sing with the letter names of the ***treble clef*** notes – sing an ***octave*** lower if the range is too high.

♪ Games:

1) Write these five notes in ***minims*** on page 62.
2) On page 23:
   a. Count the ***treble clef staccato markings***.
   b. Circle the stepwise notes ***G-F-E-D-C***.

♪ Pointers:

Do you have good hand shape?
Are you playing the double notes in the ***bass clef*** clearly?

Tweedledee's - 'Contrariwise!'

What is embroidered on Tweedledee's collar?

Date:________________

♪ Notes in the Treble Clef: C, D, E, F & G

At this point of study, play the black key on the left of E note on bars 5 and 7 as written. This note is known as E flat. Can you remember playing this note in Book 1 on page 15? Can you describe the mood? Tweedledum's new white rattle has broken!

♪ Play & Sing Along

Let's play and sing with the letter names of the ***treble clef*** notes – sing an ***octave*** lower if the range is too high.

♪ Games:

On page 25:

a. Circle the stepwise notes ***C-D-E-F-G***.
b. How many ***phrases*** are there?

♪ Pointers:

Do you have good hand-shape?
Can you hear your left hand clearly?
Are you playing the double notes in the ***bass clef*** together?
Are you playing ***legato***?
Are you playing E ***flat*** notes with finger 3?

Tweedledum's New White Rattle

Who breaks Tweedledum's new white rattle?

Date:________________

Part Three C, D, E, F & G in the Bass Clef

Can you locate the C note between the 2nd and 3rd lines of the ***bass clef***? (Hint: Use the same hand position for *Stepping Up and Down the Looking-Glass)*. Your teacher will show you the C hand position on your left hand.

♪ Play & Sing Along

When you can play this piece very well, let's play the melody line in ***unison*** an ***octave*** apart.
Let's play and sing the melody line.

♪ Games:

On page 27:

a. Circle the C notes in the ***bass clef***.
b. Circle the stepwise notes ***C-D-E-F-G*** in the ***bass clef***.
c. Write the notes in the ***treble clef***.

♪ Pointers:

Are both hands in C position before you start playing?
Are you playing both hands together?
Are you playing ***legato***?

Music by Fiddles and Fiddle-Sticks

Smooth bowing

Alice Chua

Who is dancing with the twins under the tree?

Date:________________

♪ Notes in the Bass Clef: C, D, E, F & G

Revision Can you prepare your C position for the left hand?

♪ Play & Sing Along

When you can play the left hand very steadily, let's play the melody line in ***unison*** an ***octave*** apart.
Let's play and sing the melody line.

♪ Games:

On page 29:

a. Write the new notes in the ***treble clef***.
b. Circle the stepwise notes ***C-D-E-F-G*** in the ***bass clef***.
c. Circle the stepwise notes ***F-E-D*** in the ***bass clef***.
d. How many ***phrases*** are there?
e. A ***minim*** equals 2 / 3 / 4 ***quavers***.

♪ Pointers:

Are you sitting comfortably?
Is your left hand in C position before you start playing?
Are you playing the notes ***legato***?
Are the ***unison*** notes sounding together?

The Tricky Walrus

Medium

Alice Chua

What kind of tricks do the Walrus and Carpenter play?

Date:_______________

♪ Notes in the Bass Clef: C, D, E, F & G

Revision Can you prepare your C position for the left hand?

♪ Repeat Sign 

When you see the first sign, the passage is to be repeated.
When you see the second sign, the part between the markings is repeated.

♪ Play & Sing Along

When you can play the left hand very steadily, let's play the melody line in ***unison*** an ***octave*** apart.
Let's play and sing the melody line.

♪ Games:

On page 31:

a. Circle the stepwise notes ***G-F-E-D-C***.
b. Draw a triangle over the C notes.

♪ Pointers:

Is your left hand in C position before you start playing?
Are you playing the ***staccato*** notes short?

The Cheeky Carpenter

Cheekily

Alice Chua

Who do the Walrus and Carpenter trick?

Date:________________

♪ Notes in the Bass Clef: C, D, E, F & G

The stepwise notes ***E-F-G*** are the basis for this composition.

♪ Play & Sing Along

Let's play the notes in *A Very Long Poem* ***legato***.

When you can play the left hand very steadily, let's play the melody line in ***unison*** an ***octave*** apart.

Let's play and sing the melody line.

♪ Games:

On page 33:

a. Circle all the stepwise ***E-F-G*** notes.
b. Mark each note with a dot above it – you have changed the ***articulation***!
c. Can you describe the mood?

♪ Pointers:

Do you have good sitting posture?

Do you have a good hand shape?

Are both hands playing together?

Are you playing ***legato***?

Are you playing ***staccato*** crisply?

A Very Long Poem

Add F♯ between the two G crotchets in bars 1, 2, 5 & 6.
Your teacher will show you how. Can you hear the difference?

Part Four Chords & Intervals

♪ C & G7 Chords

A ***chord*** is made up of two or more notes.

C ***chord*** is made up of three notes, ***C-E-G***, and is played with fingers **5-3-1** of the left hand.

G_7 ***chord*** is made up of four notes, ***G-B-D-F***, but at this level we are playing in ***B-F-G*** position, using fingers **5-2-1** of the left hand. You will need to stretch your fifth finger to reach the B note. (Hint: the left hand has the same position as *A Very Long Poem* on page 33).

♪ Composition

With these ***chord*** stimuli (C and G7 chords) we are going to compose and notate the melody on page 35. Now play and sing along with your composition.

♪ Pointers:

Do you have good hand-shape?

Are you playing the three notes of each ***chord*** clearly?

Can you remember the notes that make up C ***chord***?

Dancing Baby Oysters

Can you draw the dancing Baby Oysters?

Date:________________

♪ C & G7 Chords

Revision

C ***chord*** is played as ***C-E-G*** with fingers **5-3-1**.

G_7 ***chord*** is played as ***B-F-G*** with fingers **5-2-1**.

♪ Composition

With these ***chord*** stimuli (C and G7 chords) we are going to compose and notate the melody on page 37. Now play and sing along with your composition.

♪ Games:

1) Write the correct ***chord*** names above the ***treble clef stave*** on the first beat of each ***bar*** in the brackets provided. If the ***chord*** is repeated from the previous ***bar***, you do not need to write it again.
2) Circle the C ***chords*** in the ***bass clef***.

♪ Pointers:

Are both hands in C position before you start playing?

Are you comfortable playing the B note in the G_7 ***chord***?

Are you playing the three notes together in ***bar*** 8?

Can you remember the notes that make up the G_7 ***chord***?

Waltzing Baby Oysters

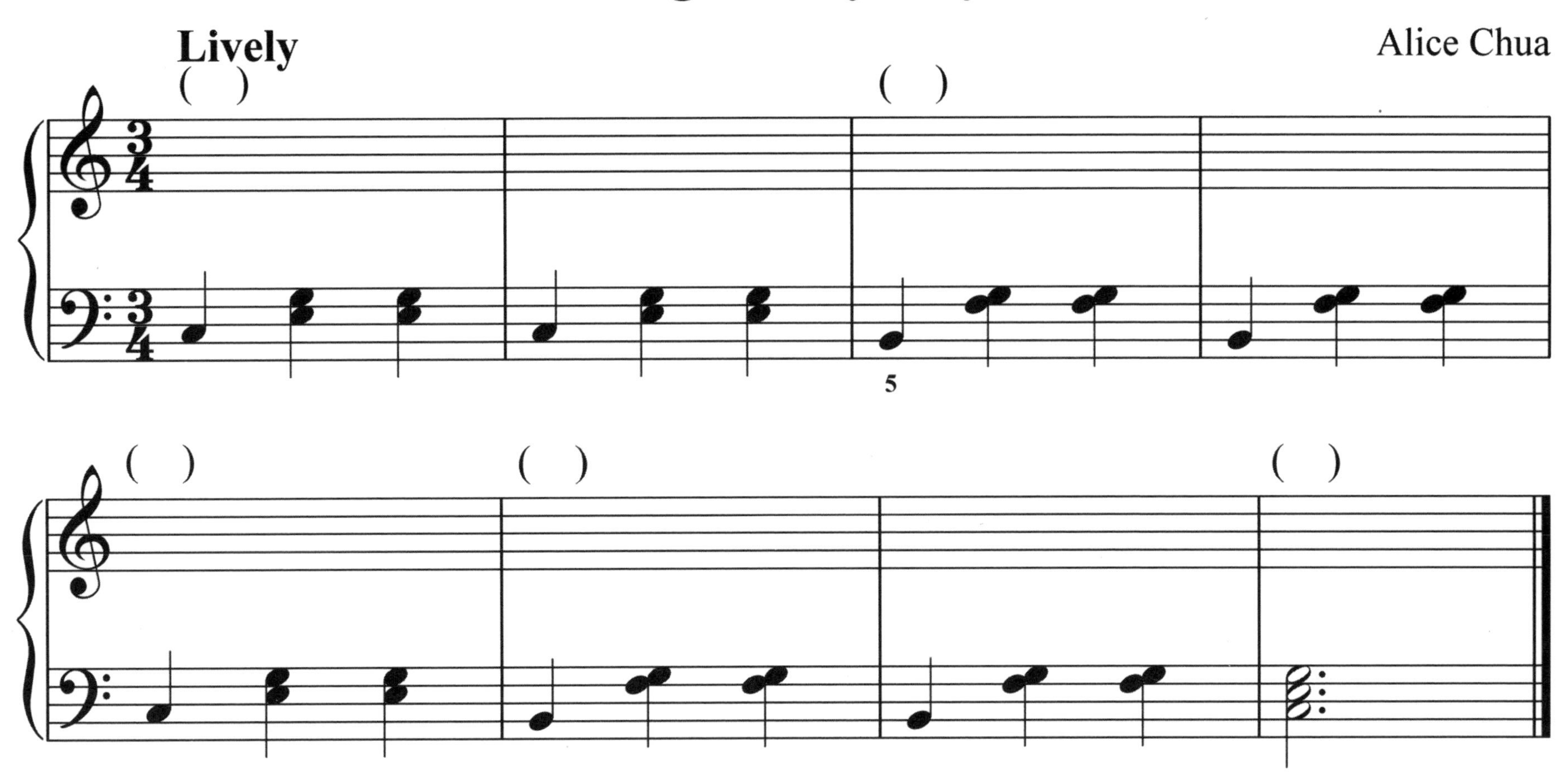

Can you draw the Baby Oysters waltzing with the Carpenter?

Date:_______________

♪ F Chord

F ***chord*** is made up of three notes, ***F-A-C***. At this level, F ***chord*** is played as ***C-F-A*** with fingers **5-2-1**. You need to stretch your thumb to reach the A note.

♪ Composition

With these ***chord*** stimuli (C, F and G7 chords) we are going to compose and notate the melody on page 39. Now play and sing along with your composition.

♪ Game:

Write the ***chord*** names above the ***treble clef stave*** on the first beat of each ***bar*** in the brackets provided. Remember, if the ***chord*** is repeated from the previous ***bar***, you do not need to write it again.

♪ Pointers:

Is your left hand in C position before you start playing?

Do you notice the different rhythm in ***bar*** 8 of *Baby Oysters' Cha-Cha-Cha*?

Are you comfortable playing the A note of the F ***chord*** with your thumb?

Baby Oysters' Cha-Cha-Cha

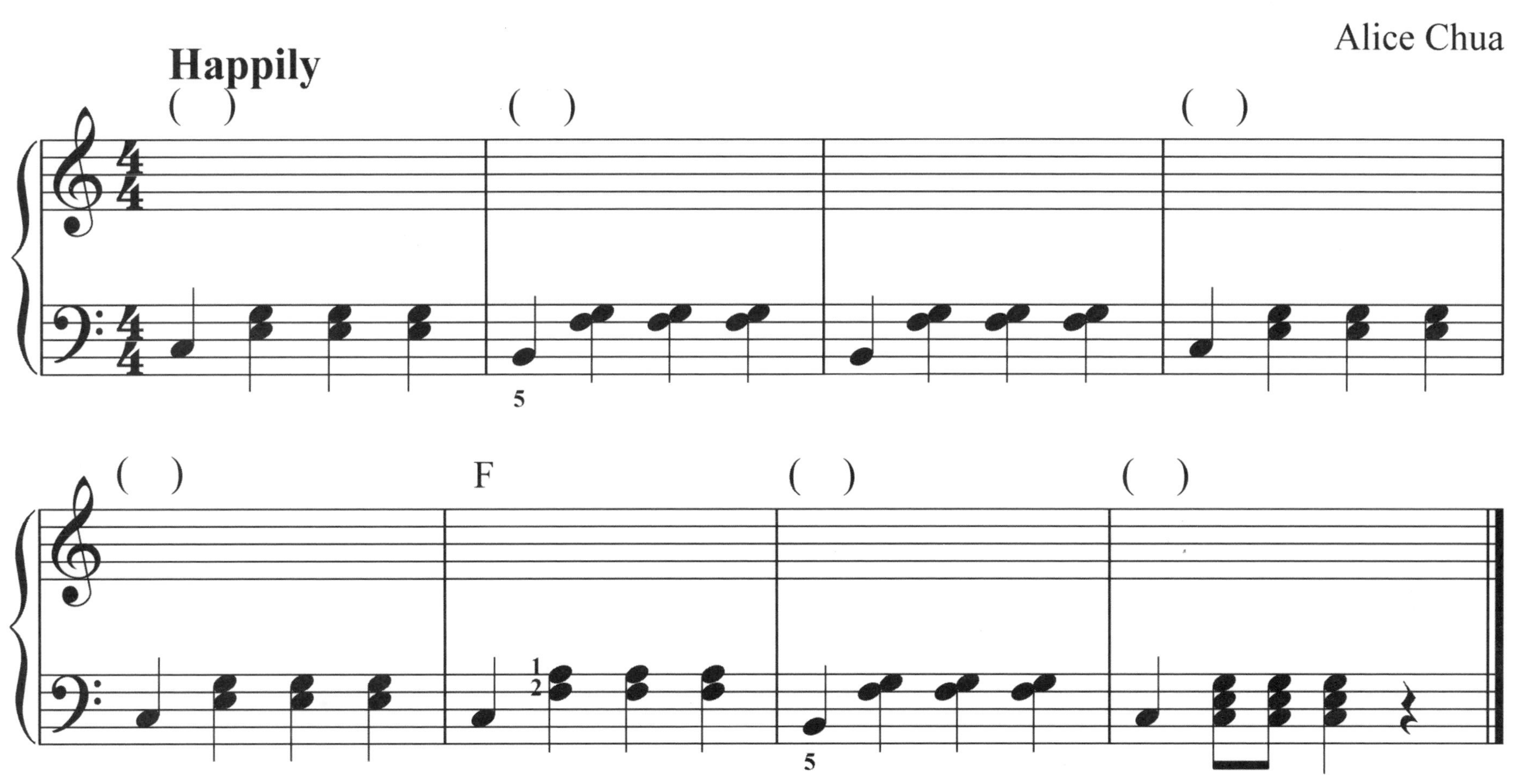

Can you draw the Baby Oysters dancing cha-cha-cha?

Date:________________

♪ Intervals – 2nd, 3rd, 4th & 5th

An ***interval*** is the distance between two different notes.

Examples:

- C to D is an ***interval*** of 2nd
- C to E is an ***interval*** of 3rd
- C to F is an ***interval*** of 4th
- C to G is an ***interval*** of 5th

♪ Play & Sing Along

Let's ***harmonise*** this tune.

Let's play the melody in ***unison*** at an ***octave*** apart.

♪ Games:

1) Let's clap the rhythm pattern of *Trotting Baby Oysters*.
2) On page 41:
   a. Mark the 2nd ***interval*** in ***bar*** 2 with a circle.
   b. Mark the 3rd ***interval*** in ***bar*** 4 with a triangle.
   c. Mark the 4th ***interval*** in ***bar*** 6 with a square.

♪ Pointers:

Do you have good hand shape?

Are you playing the ***quavers*** evenly?

Trotting Baby Oysters

Why are the Baby Oysters trotting very quickly on the hot sand?

Part Five Scales & Broken Chords

♪ Scale of C major

A ***scale*** is made up of 8 notes or ***degrees***, and it is like a ladder; notes can ascend (go up) or descend (go down). Your teacher will now play the ***scale*** of C major ascending and descending. Watch closely how your teacher plays this ***scale***.

♪ Play & Sing Along

Play and sing the C major ***scale***.

♪ Games:

On page 43:

a. Name the ***interval*** of the last two notes in the ***bass clef***.
b. Can you improvise two ***bars*** using the notes ***E-F-G*** as the basis of your composition?

♪ Pointer:

Are you playing the notes evenly?

Scaling Up to Humpty Dumpty's C House

Medium

Alice Chua

Where does Humpty Dumpty wear his beautiful cravat?

Date:________________

♪ Scale of C major

Now you are going to play the ***scale*** of C major ascending and descending. Your teacher will show you how to play the ***scale***. Watch the fingering carefully.

♪ Broken Chord of C major

You have played the ***broken chord*** of C major with your left hand in *Dancing Baby Oysters* on page 35. Let's play the ***broken chord*** of C major with your right hand using finger number **1-2-3-5** on ascending notes ***C-E-G-C***.

♪ Games:

1) Write the fingering for *The Lion and The Unicorn*.
2) On page 63, write the ***scale*** of C major ascending in the ***treble clef*** in ***semibreves*** and descending in the ***bass clef*** in ***minims***.
3) Can you clap a two-***bar*** pattern as an answer to your teacher's rhythm?

♪ Pointers:

Are you playing the ***broken chords*** with a relaxed wrist?
Are you playing the ***broken chords*** with the correct fingering?

The Lion and the Unicorn

Who wins the fight for the crown?

Date:_______________

♪ Scale of G major

C major ***scale*** ascending starts from Middle C and ends on High C.

Likewise, G major ***scale*** ascending starts on G note and ends on High G, an ***octave*** apart. Play the ***scale*** of G major ascending using the same fingering. Listen carefully; can you detect an odd note?

The seventh note needs to be played on a black key – this note is called F ***sharp***. A ***sharp*** raises a note by a ***semitone***.

The ***key signature*** of G major is F ***sharp***.

On page 47, there is a new note in the ***bass clef stave*** – D note. The new position for your left hand is G position.

♪ Play & Sing Along

Play and sing the G major ***scale***.

♪ Game:

Write the fingering above the notes of G major ***scale*** on page 47.

♪ Pointer:

Are you reaching the F ***sharp*** comfortably?

Scaling Up to Humpty Dumpty's G House

Who gives Humpty Dumpty the beautiful cravat?

Date:_______________

𝅘𝅥𝅮 Scale of G major

Now you are going to play the ***scale*** of G major ascending and descending.

𝅘𝅥𝅮 Broken Chord of G major

You have played the ***broken chord*** of C major in *The Lion and The Unicorn* on page 45.

Let's play the ***broken chord*** of G major with your right hand using the same fingering as for C major. Can you sing along?

𝅘𝅥𝅮 Games:

1) What is the ***key signature*** of G major?
2) Write the ***scale*** of G major ascending in the ***bass clef*** in ***semibreves*** and descending in the ***treble clef*** in ***crotchets*** on page 63. Do not use ***key signature***.
3) Can you improvise two ***bars*** using the notes ***B-A-G*** as the basis of your composition?

𝅘𝅥𝅮 Pointers:

Are you playing the ***scale legato***?

Are you playing the ***broken chords legato***?

Messengers Haigha and Hatta

Why does the White King need two messengers?

Date:________________

♪ Scale of D major

D major ***scale*** ascending starts from D note and ends on High D at an ***octave*** apart.

The ***key signature*** of D major is F ***sharp*** and C ***sharp***.

The new position for your left hand is D position.

♪ Play & Sing Along

Play and sing the D major ***scale***.

♪ Games:

1) If the 1st ***degree*** of D major ***scale*** is D note:
   a. What is the 3rd ***degree***?
   b. What is the 7th ***degree***?
2) What is the ***key signature*** of D major?
3) Can you improvise two ***bars*** using the notes ***G-A-B*** as the basis of your composition?
4) Can you clap a two-***bar*** pattern as an answer to your teacher's rhythm?

♪ Pointers:

Are you using the correct fingering?

Remember to play F sharp and C sharp.

Scaling Up to Humpty Dumpty's D House

Why is Humpty Dumpty given the cravat?

𝅘𝅥𝅮 Scale of D major

Now you are going to play the ***scale*** of D major ascending and descending.

𝅘𝅥𝅮 Broken Chord of D major

You have played the ***broken chord*** of G major in *Messengers Haigha and Hatta* on page 49.

Let's play the ***broken chord*** of D major with your right hand using the same fingering as for G major. Can you sing along?

𝅘𝅥𝅮 Games:

1) Write the ***scale*** of D major descending in the ***treble clef*** in ***semibreves*** and ascending in the ***bass clef*** in ***crotchets*** on page 64. Do not use ***key signature***.
2) What is the ***key signature*** of D major?
3) Can you improvise four ***bars*** using the notes ***B-A-G*** as the basis of your composition?

𝅘𝅥𝅮 Pointers:

Are you playing the ***semibreves*** to their full values?

Are you playing the ***scales*** with the correct fingering?

Ham-Sandwiches and Hay

Who is given Ham-Sandwiches and Hay?

Date:_______________

♪ Scale of F major

F major ***scale*** ascending starts from F note and ends on High F an ***octave*** apart.

F major fingering for the right hand is slightly different. The finger numbers used are **1-2-3-4-1-2-3-4**. The fourth note needs to be played on a black key – this note is called B ***flat***. A ***flat*** lowers a note by a ***semitone***. Watch closely how your teacher plays this ***scale***. The new position for your left hand is F position.

The ***key signature*** of F major is B ***flat***.

♪ Play & Sing Along

Play and sing the ***scale*** of F major.

♪ Games:

On page 55:

a. Which ***bars*** contain B ***flat***?
b. Can you improvise four ***bars*** using the notes ***F-G-A*** as the basis for your composition?

♪ Pointer:

Are you playing with the correct fingering?

Scaling Up to Humpty Dumpty's F House

Can you draw Humpty-Dumpty sitting on the wall?

Date:________________

𝅘𝅥𝅮 Scale of F major

Now you are going to play the ***scale*** of F major ascending and descending.

𝅘𝅥𝅮 Broken Chord of F major

You have played the ***broken chord*** of D major in *Ham-Sandwiches and Hay* on page 53.

Let's play the ***broken chord*** of F major with your right hand using the same fingering as for D major. Can you sing along?

𝅘𝅥𝅮 Games:

1) Write the ***scale*** of F major ascending in the ***bass clef*** in ***semibreves*** and descending in the ***treble clef*** in ***minims*** on page 64. Do not use ***key signature***.
2) Can you improvise four ***bars*** using the notes ***E-F-E*** as the basis of your composition?
3) Can you clap a two-***bar*** pattern as an answer to your teacher's rhythm?

𝅘𝅥𝅮 Pointer:

Can you remember the new fingering?

Looking-Glass Cake

Who is cutting the Looking-Glass cake for the King, Lion and the Unicorn?

Shaking and Waking

Piano Duet (Secondo)

Brightly

Alice Chua

Which kitten is the White Queen?

Shaking and Waking

Piano Duet (Primo)

Brightly
Play both hands one octave higher

Alice Chua

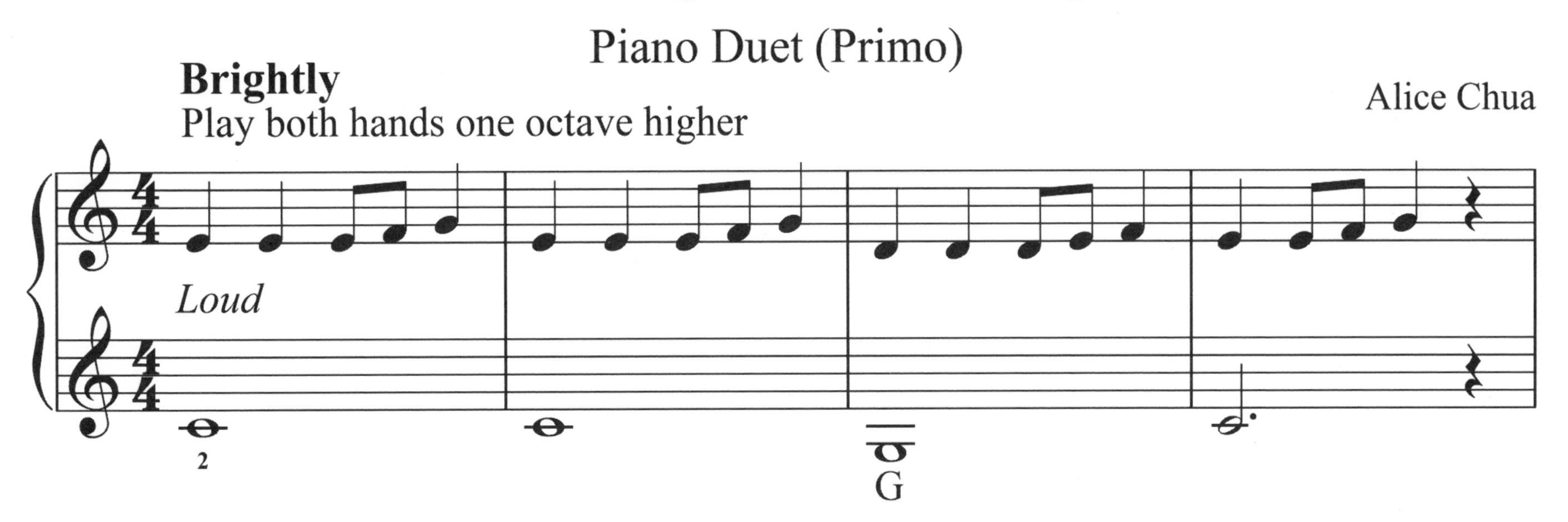

Which kitten is the Red Queen?

The King's Memorandum Book

Piano Duet (Secondo)

Majestically

Alice Chua

Can you draw the King's memorandum book?

The King's Memorandum Book

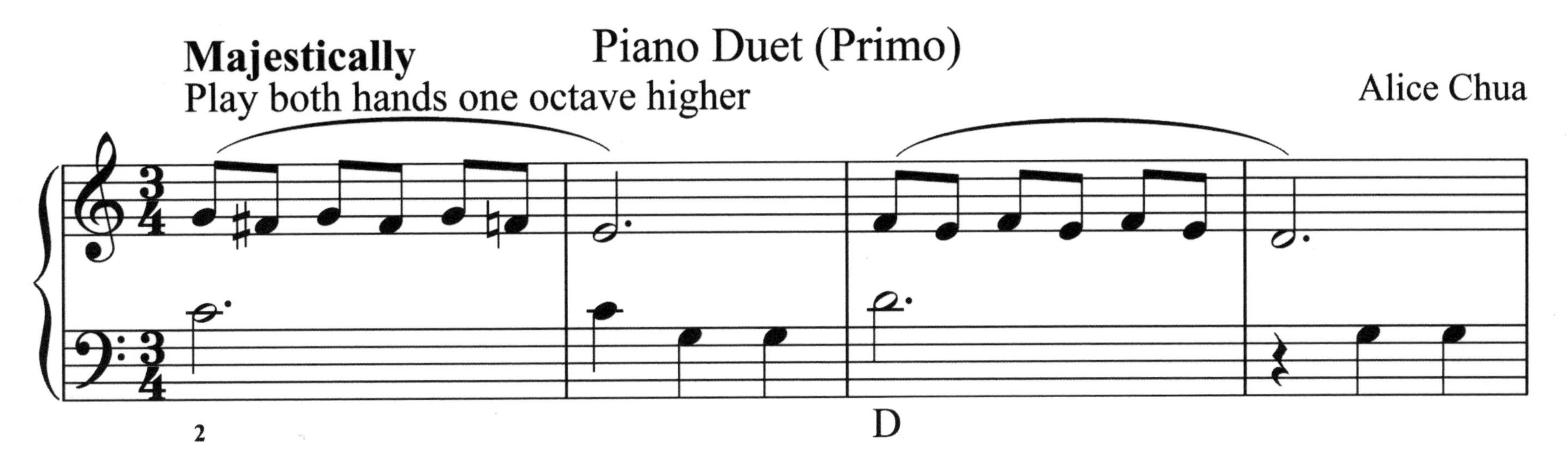

Can you sing along this beautiful tune?